MUM – I FEEL FUNNY!

A family guide to common ailments

Ann McPherson and Aidan Macfarlane

Drawn by Nicholas Garland

Chatto & Windus · London · 1982

Published by Chatto & Windus Ltd
40 William IV Street, London WC2N 4DF

Clarke, Irwin & Co Ltd, Toronto

British Library Cataloguing in Publication Data
McPherson, Ann
   Mum – I feel funny!
   1. Children – care and hygiene
   I. Title   II. Macfarlane Aidan
   613'. 0432' 0240431 RJ101

   ISBN 0 7011 2631 0

Text © Ann McPherson and Aidan Macfarlane 1982
Drawings © Nicholas Garland 1982

Printed in Great Britain by
Mansell Bookbinders Limited
Witham, Essex

For

Alexander

Beth

Gussie

Magnus

Sam

Tamara

Tess

Theo

Emily

and Tim

We all get ill at fairly regular intervals, and children are no exception. In most cases these illnesses are not serious, but they are often worrying, both to the parents and to the children themselves. As doctors we find ourselves constantly explaining what causes complaints such as sore throats, headaches, and coughs and colds, and how they can be treated. So the idea came to us of writing a simple, practical guide to common family ailments, in strip cartoon form especially for children (but also their parents), about the causes, symptoms and course of each illness, how it can be dealt with and when the doctor needs to be consulted. We hope *Mum – I Feel Funny!* will prove to be entertaining and take at least some of the worry out of these unpleasant but minor everyday illnesses.

Ann McPherson
Aidan Macfarlane
Oxford, February 1982

Contents

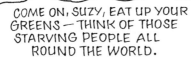

HULLO, DOCTOR...

...AND THEY NEED PLENTY TO DRINK BECAUSE THEY LOSE SO MUCH WATER WITH ALL THAT DIARRHOEA.

BUT ONLY GIVE THEM A LITTLE AT A TIME, AND NO MILK BECAUSE AN UPSET TUMMY CAN'T DIGEST IT. NOTHING TO EAT.

...AND THE DOCTOR SAYS NOTHING TO EAT AND IT'S QUITE COMMON TO GET CRAMPY TUMMY PAINS. AND... UM OH YES, SHE SAYS WE MAY CATCH IT TOO.

OH NO.

...AND SHE SAID WE COULD GIVE SUZY A TEASPOONFUL OF KAOLIN EVERY TWO TO THREE HOURS TO HELP DRY THE DIARRHOEA UP.

THIS BOOK SAYS THAT DIARRHOEA OR SICKNESS OR BOTH ARE USUALLY CAUSED BY VIRUSES OR BACTERIA, WHICH ARE TINY LITTLE BUGS — ERR! THAT MEANS YOU'VE GOT BUGS— WHICH WE CATCH FROM OTHER PEOPLE. IT SAYS THESE CAN BE BREATHED IN OR SWALLOWED SO THAT SEVERAL MEMBERS OF A FAMILY MAY GET IT.

...AND MUM WAS RIGHT ABOUT WASHING YOUR HANDS BECAUSE IT SAYS HERE THAT BUGS CAN BE CARRIED BY FLIES ON YOUR FINGERS OR IN FOOD. YUK!

ONE WEEK LATER...

COR, MUM, I'M STARVING. CAN I HAVE SOME MORE?

AT LEAST I DIDN'T HAVE TO COOK WHEN THEY WERE ILL.

COUGHS AND COLDS

GO AND HURRY TIM UP.

MUM SAYS HURRY UP.

I AM.

I WONDER IF WE OUGHT TO KEEP HIM OFF SCHOOL. HE WAS COUGHING ALL NIGHT.

OH, HE'S ALL RIGHT. BUT PERHAPS WE SHOULD TAKE HIM TO THE DOCTOR'S IF HE'S STILL COUGHING THIS EVENING.

AFTER SCHOOL...

YOU'LL ONLY FEEL WORSE IF YOU GO OUT TO FOOTBALL WITH THAT COUGH IN THIS WEATHER.

I BET I LOSE MY PLACE IN THE TEAM. I SUPPOSE IT'S ANOTHER OF THOSE BEASTLY VIRUSES THAT'S GIVEN ME MY COLD.

SURGERY HOURS

PLEASE RING AND ENTER

IT STARTED AS A COLD, AND HE'S KEPT US AWAKE COUGHING AT NIGHT ALL THIS WEEK.

...AND NOW THE BABY'S GOT IT TOO. WOULD SOME COUGH MEDICINE HELP?

COUGH MEDICINE RARELY HELPS. BUT IF YOU MAKE HIS ROOM STEAMY BY BOILING A KETTLE — ONLY BE VERY CAREFUL WITH THE BABY — THAT WILL LOOSEN THE MUCUS IN HIS NOSE. I'LL JUST LISTEN TO HIS CHEST TO MAKE SURE THERE'S NO INFECTION DOWN THERE.

THERE'S NO INFECTION ON HIS CHEST, IT'S JUST IN HIS NOSE AND THROAT AND IT'LL GET BETTER ANYWAY.

I'M AFRAID NO ONE'S FOUND A CURE FOR COLDS YET, BUT AT LEAST THERE ARE WAYS OF MAKING TIM **FEEL** BETTER.

GIVE HIM AN ASPIRIN EVERY FOUR HOURS— HE DOESN'T HAVE TO STAY OFF SCHOOL UNLESS HE FEELS ROTTEN.

THE COUGH IS CAUSED BY MUCUS DRIPPING DOWN THE BACK OF HIS THROAT. TIM OUGHT TO BLOW HIS NOSE AS OFTEN AS POSSIBLE.

WHAT'S MUCUS?

YOU WOULD PROBABLY CALL IT SNOT.

YUKK!

COLDS ARE CAUSED BY VIRUSES AND NOT BY ACTUALLY GETTING COLD, SO TIM CAN GO BACK TO PLAYING FOOTBALL AS SOON AS HE FEELS BETTER

OH, GOOD, THEN I THINK I FEEL BETTER ALREADY!

BLOW YOUR NOSE, TIM, BEFORE YOU GO TO BED.

GET RID OF THAT SLIME.

EEURK! SHUT UP, SUZY—I'LL GIVE YOU SOME FOR YOUR BIRTHDAY!

ANOTHER BAD NIGHT. I WISH IT WOULD HURRY UP AND GET BETTER LIKE THE DOCTOR SAID IT WOULD.

COUGH COUGH COUGH

FLU

LET'S GET OUR BOOTS ON AND MAKE A SNOWMAN.

I'M NOT COMING.

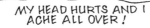

MY HEAD HURTS AND I ACHE ALL OVER!

YES, YOU DO FEEL HOT. WHY DON'T YOU LIE DOWN?

HULLO, I FEEL SHIVERY AND AWFUL.

HULLO, DARLING SUZY'S ILL TOO. I'LL CALL THE DOCTOR FOR YOU BOTH.

...AND HER TEMPERATURE IS 38.5— IS IT SERIOUS, DOCTOR?

ALL THESE THINGS, INCLUDING THE TEMPERATURE, ARE WHAT YOU USUALLY GET WITH FLU— LOTS OF PEOPLE HAVE IT AT THE MOMENT, AND THAT'S WHAT SHE'S GOT.

...YOU JUST NEED LOTS OF DRINKS AND AN ASPIRIN EVERY FOUR HOURS AND YOU'LL SOON FEEL BETTER.

THEY CAN GET UP AS SOON AS THEY FEEL LIKE IT AND IF ANY OF THE REST OF YOU GET IT, YOU DON'T NEED TO CALL ME.

WHAT IS FLU, MUM, DOES IT SORT OF FLY?

FLU IS SHORT FOR INFLUENZA AND IS CAUSED BY ANOTHER OF THOSE LITTLE BUGS CALLED VIRUSES.

9

GERMAN MEASLES

HEY, MUM, WHAT'S GERMAN MEASLES?

WHY?

COZ THE THIRD YEAR GIRLS HAD INJECTIONS AGAINST IT AT SCHOOL TODAY.

NO ROLLER SKATING NO CYCLING

YOU GET A SPOTTY RASH ALL OVER. TIM HAD IT LAST YEAR—HE WASN'T VERY ILL.

WAS THAT THE TIME YOU TOOK ME TO THE DOCTOR AND SHE WASN'T SURE WHAT IT WAS?

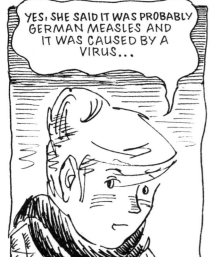

YES, SHE SAID IT WAS PROBABLY GERMAN MEASLES AND IT WAS CAUSED BY A VIRUS...

... BUT SHE SAID IT'S DIFFICULT TO TELL BECAUSE MANY OTHER VIRUSES CAN GIVE YOU THE SAME KIND OF RASH.

SO WHY DO YOU NEED AN INJECTION AGAINST IT?

TO STOP YOU CATCHING IT WHEN YOU'RE OLDER.

BUT ONLY THE GIRLS GOT THE INJECTIONS.

MEASLES

HE DIDN'T SEEM TO ENJOY IT MUCH — I DON'T KNOW WHETHER HE DOESN'T FEEL WELL OR WHETHER THERE WERE JUST TOO MANY GIRLS.

WHAT DO YOU SAY, JOHNNY?

HE'S HAD A BIT OF A COLD AND SORE EYES FOR A FEW DAYS — HE EVEN HAD A FEVER LAST NIGHT, BUT HE DID SO WANT TO COME TODAY!

THANK YOU FOR HAVING ME.

NEXT DAY...

NO, POOR JOHNNY HAS GOT THE MEASLES, THAT'S WHY HE'S BEEN FEELING ROTTEN FOR THE LAST FEW DAYS — IT USUALLY STARTS LIKE THAT.

NOT US THIS TIME THEN, DOCTOR?

LUCKY I GAVE YOUR BABY HIS INJECTION AGAINST MEASLES LAST WEEK.

WHAT CAUSES MEASLES? WILL HE DIE?

DO YOU GET SPOTS? HOW DOES THE INJECTION STOP IT?

ONE QUESTON AT A TIME, PLEASE. MEASLES IS CAUSED BY A VIRUS—YES, YOU DO GET SPOTS—NO, JOHNNY WON'T DIE, BUT HE DOESN'T FEEL VERY **WELL AT THE MOMENT!**

IS THIS BRITISH MEASLES?

NO, THIS ONE IS JUST CALLED MEASLES AND THE INJECTION WHICH YOU HAD WHEN YOU WERE A BABY GIVES YOU VERY MILD MEASLES AND USUALLY STOPS YOU FROM GETTING IT AGAIN LATER.

WILL HE BE AWAY FROM SCHOOL?

HE'LL BE AWAY FROM SCHOOL FOR ABOUT A WEEK UNTIL THE SPOTS HAVE GONE.

OH, NO, HE'LL MISS THE FOOTBALL TRIALS.

I HOPE EVERYBODY WHO WAS AT THE PARTY DOESN'T GO DOWN WITH MEASLES.

WELL, AT LEAST MY TWO WON'T GET IT AS THEY'VE HAD THEIR INJECTIONS. PITY JOHNNY DIDN'T HAVE HIS.

CUTS AND BRUISES

I'M GLAD YOU'RE BETTER AGAIN, JOHNNY. SUZY, I BET YOU CAN'T DO THIS.

I BET I CAN.

Wheeeeweee

Aghhhhh

IT'S ALL YOUR FAULT, TIM.

I DIDN'T MEAN TO — QUICK, GET MUM.

COR, BLOOD!

HAVE I BROKEN MY LEG?

LET'S SEE WHAT THE DAMAGE IS. I REMEMBER THE DOCTOR SAYING THAT IF YOU CAN WALK ON IT IMMEDIATELY, THEN IT'S PROBABLY NOT BROKEN.

ONE OF YOUR KNEES IS CUT AND THE OTHER ONE'S RATHER BRUISED AND GRAZED.

I BANGED MY HEAD AND THAT HURTS TOO.

HOLD THIS CLEAN HANDKER-CHIEF HARD OVER THE CUT ON YOUR KNEE TO STOP THE BLEEDING. I'LL GO AND GET SOME WARM WATER TO CLEAN UP THE CUT AND THE GRAZE.

I KNOW IT HURTS, BUT I MUST GET ALL THE DIRT OUT OR IT WILL GET INFECTED.

DO YOU THINK IT NEEDS A STITCH?

I DON'T WANT TO BE STITCHED!

I THINK WE'D BETTER LET THE DOCTOR DECIDE ABOUT THAT. THERE'S A BRAVE GIRL.

AGHH!

NO, I THINK THE CUT IS SMALL ENOUGH TO HEAL BY ITSELF NOW THAT YOU'VE CLEANED IT SO WELL. BY THE WAY, HAS SHE HAD A RECENT INJECTION AGAINST TETANUS?

YES.

WHAT'S TETANUS?

TETANUS IS CAUSED BY BACTERIA WHICH LIVE IN THE GROUND AND IF THEY GET INTO THE WOUND THEY CAN MAKE YOU VERY ILL. BUT NOW THAT YOU HAVE AN INJECTION AGAINST IT, IT RARELY HAPPENS.

GOOD OLD MUM, GETTING ALL OUR INJECTIONS DONE.

NOW WHAT ABOUT THIS BUMP ON HER HEAD? IT'S LUCKY SHE WASN'T KNOCKED OUT OR ELSE SHE WOULD HAVE TO GO INTO HOSPITAL TO MAKE SURE THAT SHE WAS ALL RIGHT AND THAT SHE HAD NOT FRACTURED HER SKULL.

BUT YOU MUST KEEP AN EYE ON HER DURING THE NEXT TWENTY-FOUR HOURS AND IF SHE SHOULD GET SICK OR FEEL DROWSY BEFORE BEDTIME, THEN CONTACT ME STRAIGHT AWAY BECAUSE IT COULD MEAN THAT SHE'S BRUISED SOMETHING INSIDE HER HEAD. AND THAT COULD BE SERIOUS.

WHAT ABOUT THE BRUISES ON HER LEG?

THEY'LL BE A BIT PAINFUL AND TURN FUNNY COLOURS, BUT THEY'LL DISAPPEAR IN A FEW DAYS. YOU COULD GIVE HER AN ASPIRIN....

AGHHHH!

HEADACHES

COME ON, SUZY—YOU'RE GETTING AS BAD AS TIM AT GETTING UP.

OH, DAD, I DON'T WANT TO—I'VE GOT A HEADACHE.

COME AND HAVE SOME BREAKFAST AND WE'LL SEE HOW YOU FEEL

WELL, YOU LOOK ALL RIGHT FOR SCHOOL. YOU WILL BE ABLE TO GO, WON'T YOU?

I DON'T WANT TO, BUT I SUPPOSE I'LL HAVE TO.

ONE WEEK LATER...

OH, WHAT'S THE MATTER NOW, SUZY?

PLEASE, MISS, I'VE GOT ANOTHER HEADACHE!

WELL, YOU HAD BETTER GO TO THE SCHOOL NURSE, THEN.

I WISH SOME NICE PERSON WOULD LOOK AFTER MY HEADACHE!

...AND THE SCHOOL NURSE GAVE ME AN ASPIRIN AND I WENT BACK INTO CLASS AND MY HEADACHE GOT BETTER.

I'M GETTING A BIT WORRIED ABOUT ALL THESE HEADACHES. I THINK I'LL TAKE YOU TO THE DOCTOR'S TO MAKE SURE THAT EVERYTHING'S ALL RIGHT.

OH, MUM, I'M OK.

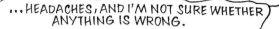

...HEADACHES, AND I'M NOT SURE WHETHER ANYTHING IS WRONG.

BECAUSE SHE'S GETTING THEM SO OFTEN YOU'RE JUST AS WELL TO HAVE HER CHECKED — NOW WHEREABOUTS ARE THEY, SUZY?

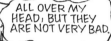

ALL OVER MY HEAD, BUT THEY ARE NOT VERY BAD.

WELL, I'VE EXAMINED HER CAREFULLY. I CAN'T FIND ANYTHING SERIOUSLY WRONG — IT'S NOTHING TO DO WITH THAT RECENT BANG ON HER HEAD, IF THAT'S WHAT YOU'RE WORRIED ABOUT.

WHY WERE YOU LOOKING INTO MY EYES.

BECAUSE WITH THIS INSTRUMENT, WHICH IS CALLED AN OPHTHALMOSCOPE, I CAN SEE WHAT'S GOING ON AT THE BACK OF YOUR EYES. YOURS LOOK NORMAL AND THAT TELLS ME THAT THERE IS NOTHING SERIOUS GOING WRONG INSIDE YOUR HEAD.

...HEADACHES ARE QUITE COMMON IN CHILDREN AND THEY ARE MORE OFTEN CAUSED BY LIFE'S UPS AND DOWNS THAN BECAUSE THERE'S ANYTHING SERIOUSLY WRONG.

WELL, I HAD NOTICED THAT THEY ALWAYS SEEM TO OCCUR ON MONDAYS AND NEVER AT THE WEEKENDS.

OH, MUM!

YES, THAT'S JUST THE SORT OF PATTERN ONE SOMETIMES SEES.

A DAY LATER...

STOP IT!

IT'S NOT FAIR!

NO, I DIDN'T!

GOSH, THIS IS WHAT GIVES ME A HEADACHE!

LOOK WHAT HE'S GOT!

LIAR!

CUT IT OUT!

19

TUMMY ACHE

HEY, MUM, WHERE ARE MY SHORTS?

I CAN'T FIND MY PLIMSOLLS.

WHERE ARE MY SOCKS?

WHY DO YOU ALWAYS LEAVE EVERYTHING TO THE LAST MINUTE?

WILL YOU BE ABLE TO COME TO SPORTS DAY TODAY, DADDY? YOU MUST RUN IN THE FATHERS' RACE.

I'LL BE THERE ANYHOW.

ARE YOU SURE YOU'VE GOT EVERYTHING?

ARE YOU FEELING ALL RIGHT, TIM?

I'VE GOT A BIT OF A TUMMY ACHE.

DO YOU THINK YOU NEED TO GO TO THE TOILET?

NO — I'VE TRIED, BUT IT ISN'T THAT.

HEY, JACK, TIM'S GOT A TUMMY ACHE — CAN YOU TAKE HIM TO THE SCHOOL NURSE WHILE I PHONE HIS MOTHER?

COR, I BET IT'S APPENDICITIS LIKE I HAD.

OH, DEAR, POOR TIM — JUST WHEN IT'S SPORTS DAY — I'LL COME AND FETCH HIM — IF IT'S THAT BAD PERHAPS I'D BETTER TAKE HIM TO THE DOCTOR'S.

LUCKY TIM — HE'LL MISS THE MATHS TEST.

IS HE GOING TO HOSPITAL?

BET HE'S NOT REALLY SICK.

HULLO—WHAT'S WRONG WITH TIM? I SEEM TO BE SEEING A LOT OF YOUR FAMILY RECENTLY.

GO ON, TIM, TELL THE DOCTOR.

I DON'T FEEL SICK OR ANYTHING, IT'S JUST THAT MY TUMMY HURTS.

WHEREABOUTS DOES IT HURT?

ALL OVER. CAN I HAVE AN ASPIRIN?

NO, IT'S NOT A GOOD IDEA TO TAKE ASPIRIN FOR TUMMY ACHE...

SO YOU'VE BEEN EATING ALL RIGHT AND YOU HAVEN'T GOT DIARRHOEA— AND IT DOESN'T HURT WHEN I PRESS HERE?

OH, YOU'VE GOT COLD HANDS—NO IT DOESN'T HURT.

WELL, IT'S NOT APPENDICITIS ANYWAY.

GOSH, THANK GOODNESS—BECAUSE JACK IN MY CLASS HAD APPENDICITIS LAST MONTH, BUT HIS TUMMY ACHE WAS WORSE!

WE DON'T KNOW THE REASON FOR A LOT OF TUMMY ACHES, BUT TIM'S MAY BE SOMETHING TO DO WITH HIM WORRYING ABOUT HIS RACE THIS AFTERNOON.

IT FEELS BETTER ALREADY.

WELL, YOU CAN GO BACK TO SCHOOL—BUT IF IT GETS WORSE, YOU SHOULD COME BACK AND SEE ME THIS EVENING.

FUNNY HOW SOON TUMMY ACHES GET FORGOTTEN—OH, HELP, I THINK I'M GETTING ONE NOW, IT'S THE MOTHER'S RACE NEXT!

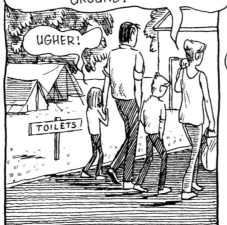

23

SORE THROAT

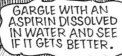

HEY, MUM, MY THROAT STILL HURTS.

GARGLE WITH AN ASPIRIN DISSOLVED IN WATER AND SEE IF IT GETS BETTER.

I CAN'T EAT THIS, MUM...

WE'LL TAKE YOUR TEMPERATURE AND YOU'D BETTER STAY IN BED TODAY.

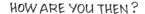

HOW ARE YOU THEN?

IT'S NOT FAIR, I'M BORED, I WANT TO GO BACK TO SCHOOL, MY THROAT'S BETTER.

LET'S SEE HOW YOU ARE TOMORROW.

GOODY, SCHOOL TODAY!

YOU SEE, I'M RIGHT, MOST THINGS GET BETTER WITHOUT NEEDING A DOCTOR.

MUM, MY THROAT HURTS.

THAT AFTERNOON,

HOW ARE YOU THEN?

OH, MUM, MY THROAT'S MUCH WORSE AND I'VE GOT LUMPS IN MY NECK AND I'VE BEEN SICK.

NEXT MORNING

HULLO, DOCTOR, MY SON HAS A VERY SORE THROAT AND HAS BEEN UNWELL FOR TWO DAYS WITH A TEMPERATURE. I'VE GIVEN HIM ASPIRIN, BUT IT'S GETTING WORSE — CAN I BRING HIM TO SEE YOU, HE'S JUST SICKING EVERYTHING UP..?

YES, YOU HAVE A NASTY SORE THROAT.

I'M GOING TO TICKLE THE BACK OF YOUR THROAT WITH THIS STICK — IT'S CALLED A SWAB AND I'LL SEND IT TO THE HOSPITAL TO SEE WHETHER YOUR SORE THROAT IS CAUSED BY A VIRUS OR BY BACTERIA.

OH, THOSE HORRID THINGS AGAIN!

I'LL START YOU OFF ON PENICILLIN WHICH YOU WILL HAVE TO TAKE FOUR TIMES A DAY. THIS WILL KILL THE BACTERIA. IF YOU HAVE A VIRUS IT WILL GET BETTER ANYWAY.

THANK YOU, DOCTOR.

MORNING

LUNCHTIME

IT'S A NUISANCE TAKING THESE PILLS FOR FIVE DAYS, BUT THE DOCTOR SAYS I MUST OR THE BUGS WON'T BE PROPERLY KILLED.

EVENING

NIGHT

HOORAY, BACK TO SCHOOL.

HOORAY, BACK TO SCHOOL.

EAR INFECTIONS

I HATE SCHOOL OUTINGS.

I'LL GIVE YOU AN ASPIRIN TO HELP THE PAIN, IF I CAN FIND ONE.

PLEASE, MISS, MY EAR HURTS.

WHY DOES SOMETHING ALWAYS HAPPEN ON OUTINGS?

DON'T SHOVE!

HURRY UP!

GET OFF MY FOOT.

ME FIRST!

POOR SUZY HAS A COLD AND NOW A BAD EARACHE. I'VE GIVEN HER AN ASPIRIN.

OH, MUM. IT STILL HURTS.

COME ON, LET'S GO DOWN TO THE DOCTOR'S NOW.

IT MUST BE VERY PAINFUL, I'M SURE WE CAN FIT YOU IN TO SEE THE DOCTOR.

RECEPTI

THE ASPIRIN MADE IT A BIT BETTER.

I WILL SHINE THIS LIGHT INTO YOUR EAR VERY CAREFULLY. IT WON'T MAKE IT HURT MORE.

CAN YOU SEE HER BRAINS, DOCTOR? IF SHE'S GOT ANY.

JUST SHUT UP, TIM. WHAT CAN YOU SEE, DOCTOR?

I CAN SEE HER EAR DRUM—IT LOOKS RED BECAUSE IT'S INFECTED—PROBABLY WITH BACTERIA. YOU OFTEN GET AN EAR INFECTION WITH A COLD.

CARRY ON GIVING HER ASPIRIN FOR THE PAIN AND HERE IS A PRESCRIPTION FOR SOME PENICILLIN TO KILL THE INFECTION.

WHAT DID SHE SAY?

OH, YES AND SHE MAY BE A BIT DEAF FOR A WHILE. SHE SHOULDN'T GO SWIMMING UNTIL IT'S BETTER, BECAUSE THE WATER COULD IRRITATE IT MORE.

REMIND ME TO REMIND YOU TO TAKE THE PENICILLIN FOUR TIMES A DAY.

CHEMIST

OPEN

NEXT DAY...

OH, GOODY, THE EARACHE'S GONE.

WHAT ABOUT YOUR BRAINS?

COME AND TAKE YOUR MEDICINE, SUZY, BEFORE YOU GO TO SCHOOL. WE'D BETTER TELL YOUR TEACHER ABOUT TAKING THE PILLS.

SHE NEVER HEARS WHEN SHE DOESN'T WANT TO.

WHAT?

TWO WEEKS LATER...

THAT'S GOOD—IT'S ALL HEALED UP AND YOU CAN GO BACK TO SWIMMING NOW.

29

CHICKEN POX

COME AND HELP ME WRITE SOME CHRISTMAS CARDS BEFORE SCHOOL.

I DON'T WANT TO, MY HEAD HURTS.

COME ON, TIM, DON'T TAKE ALL DAY

I DON'T FEEL LIKE GOING TO SCHOOL— DO I HAVE TO?

STOP FUSSING!

MEANIE, POOR TIM.

AT SCHOOL...

...HE'S NOT FEELING VERY WELL—IT LOOKS LIKE CHICKEN POX, HE'S COVERED IN SPOTS...

NURSE

OK, I'LL COME AND FETCH HIM RIGHT AWAY.

OH, NO!

SEE, I WAS RIGHT. POOR TIM.

DOES IT COME FROM CHICKENS, MUM?

NO, IT'S JUST ANOTHER OF THOSE TINY VIRUSES WHICH YOU BREATHE IN FROM SOMEONE WHO'S GOT IT.

Antibiotics are medicines made by scientists and used by doctors to kill bacteria. They do not kill viruses. Some of the commonly used antibiotics (which can be taken either as liquids or tablets) are penicillin, amoxycillin and ampicillin. They have to be taken regularly for several days even though you are feeling better or else the bacteria won't be killed properly and will make you feel ill again.

Aspirin is a drug which can be bought at the chemist's and lots of other shops. If you are ill or have a pain, it makes you feel better and brings down your temperature for a few hours, but it does not stop infection or kill bacteria or viruses. There are a number of different forms of aspirin, some of which dissolve easily in water – also another very similar medicine called paracetamol, which comes either as a liquid or as tablets. If you take too much aspirin it can be very dangerous, so it is important always to read the instructions on the bottle so that you know how much to take and how often to take it. You should never take aspirin without asking a grown-up.

Bacteria are tiny bugs, smaller even than a speck of dust. They are everywhere – but only cause us trouble when they get into our bodies. Even then, special blood cells in our bodies can usually kill them off. If this doesn't happen, then the bacteria multiply and make us ill. They are killed by antibiotics.

Infections occur when bacteria or viruses get into our bodies – usually by our breathing them in or swallowing them, or by their getting in through a cut or scrape. If they are not killed off immediately, then the bacteria or viruses begin to multiply and make us ill.

Temperature Our bodies are normally at a temperature of 37 degrees centigrade, which is hotter than the air around us. When our bodies are fighting infections they get hotter still. This is usually referred to as "having a temperature" – although this may make us feel rotten, it doesn't generally do any harm.

A *Thermometer* is used to measure the body's temperature to see if it is hotter than 37 degrees centigrade. Usually the thermometer is put in your mouth, and although it is best not to eat it, if it does accidentally break whilst in your mouth, the liquid inside won't do you any harm.

Viruses are different kinds of bugs and they are even smaller than bacteria. They are also everywhere, but only cause trouble when they get into our bodies – they are not killed by antibiotics, but our bodies are usually quite good at getting rid of them.

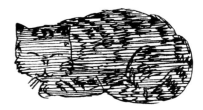